Midsommar Sól

A MIDSUMMER STORY

BY JENNIFER HARTMAN

In a wonderful place called Gimlé, there lives a young lady with hair of gold. She pulls the sun across the sky, and her name is Sól.

Sól works very hard to make sure daylight fills the skies so all the hardworking people of the world can do their chores well.

During the longest and brightest day of the year, Sól decides everyone needs a break. She leaves the sun high in the sky and joins the people below.

Townsfolk are gathered at the Tinget where important decisions are made. Together they decide they will hold their Midsommar festival today!

There will be singing and dancing and fun to be had. Whoever dances the longest will be crowned king or queen of the day.

Before the fun can begin, there is much to do. Sól helps make flower crowns worthy of royalty, while others help raise a leafy pole to sing and dance around.

Now the preparations are finished, it is time to play. The children all gather around the pole for a special song and dance.

"The little pigs, the little pigs,
they are funny to see.
Two ears, two ears, and a tail.
They are funny to see."

The townspeople sing, dance, and cheer. Everyone is having fun. There has been a lot of celebrating, but the day is almost done.

Sól is the last person dancing, which means she has won the Midsommar crown! The townspeople decree her queen of the day, and together they all cheer.

"Hurray, hurray for Midsommar Sól,
our Midsommar queen decreed!
Hurray, hurray for Midsommar Sól,
our midsummer queen indeed!"

Now that the contest is over and everyone has had their fun, Midsommar Sól leaves to pull the sun away so the night may finally come.

Fun Facts

A *Tinget* (Swedish for "thing") is a public meeting place in Sweden. It can be a building or an outdoor area where communities gather to create laws and celebrate special days.

Stories of Sól have been told for more than 2,000 years. She also appears in German mythology, where her name is Sunna.

In Norse mythology, Sól rides her chariot around the world, pulling the sun behind her to keep it from being eaten by a wolf named Skoll. In some areas, she appears to be the sun itself.

Sól has a daughter—also named Sól—who inherited the same power. The younger Sól lives in the mythical place called Gimlé. This book is based on the younger Sól.

Midsommar (Swedish for midsummer) has been celebrated for over 800 years. We know this because of engravings found on a wooden staff called a runstav.

Midsommarfest is a modern midsummer festival that celebrates the middle of summer. Some areas celebrate it for a day, a week, or even a month.

The song "Små Grodorna" ("Little Frogs") is very popular at Midsommarfest. It has a special dance.

In the northern parts of Scandinavia (and other arctic areas around the world), the sun never sets in the summer. It is called the midnight sun.

In this story, Sól comes down to join in the traditional practices of sun worship and sun games. In traditional mythology, Sól does not come down from the sky.

For more fun facts on Midsommar Sól, Midsommar, and Norse mythology, visit www.pagankids.org. You can also connect with author Jennifer Hartman on Instagram, Facebook, and Pinterest: @pagankids.

CPSIA information can be obtained
at www.ICGtesting.com
Printed in the USA
LVHW021133251022
731419LV00002B/96